# *CogAT®* Practice Test Level 8 - Instructions (Form 7)

Illustrations by: Kenneth Sommer
Written and published by: Bright Kids NYC

The Cognitive Abilities Test® (*CogAT®*) is a registered trademark of Houghton Mifflin Company, which was not involved in the production of, and neither endorses nor supports the content of this *CogAT* ® Practice Test.

Bright Kids NYC Inc.
www.brightkidsnyc.com
info@brightkidsnyc.com
917-539-4575

## About Bright Kids NYC

Bright Kids NYC was founded in New York City to provide language arts and math enrichment for young children, and to educate parents about standardized tests through workshops and consultations, as well as to prepare young children for such tests through assessments, tutoring, and publications. Our philosophy is that regardless of age, test-taking is a skill that can be acquired and mastered through practice.

At Bright Kids NYC, we strive to provide the best learning materials. Our publications are truly unique. First, all of our books have been created by qualified psychologists, learning specialists, and teachers. Second, our books have been tested by hundreds of children in our tutoring practice. Since children can make associations that many adults cannot, testing of materials by children is critical to creating successful test preparation guides. Finally, our learning specialists and teaching staff have provided practical strategies and tips so that parents can prepare their children to succeed on standardized tests.

Feel free to contact us should you have any questions.

Bright Kids NYC Inc.

Phone: 917-539-4575
Email: info@brightkidsnyc.com
www.brightkidsnyc.com
www.twitter.com/brightkids

*CogAT*® **Practice Test Level 8 - Instructions** Bright Kids NYC Inc ©

# Introduction

Bright Kids NYC created the *CogAT®* Practice Test to familiarize children with the content and the format of the *CogAT®*. Children, no matter how bright they are, do not always perform well when they are not accustomed to the format and the structure of a test. Children can misunderstand the directions, fail to look at all the answer choices, and may not always listen carefully to the questions. Thus, without adequate preparation and familiarization, children may not always perform to the best of their ability on standardized tests such as the *CogAT®*.

This Bright Kids *CogAT®* Practice Test is not designed to generate a score or a stanine as the test has not been standardized with the actual *CogAT®* norms and standards. The objective of the practice test is to identify your child's strengths and weaknesses and test taking ability so that you can prepare your child adequately for the actual test.

In order to maximize the effectiveness of the Bright Kids *CogAT®* Practice Test, it is important to first familiarize yourself with the test and its instructions. In addition, it is recommended that you designate a quiet place to work with your child, ideally in a neutral environment free of noise and clutter. Finally, provide a comfortable and proper seating arrangement to enable your child to focus and concentrate to the best of his or her ability.

Children will be taking many standardized tests throughout their school years. Teaching your child critical thinking skills along with test taking strategies at a young age will benefit your child for many years to come. Our philosophy is that regardless of age, test-taking is a skill that can be acquired and mastered through practice.

**CogAT® Practice Test Level 8 - Instructions**

Bright Kids NYC Inc ©

## _CogAT®_ Form 7 Overview

The _Cognitive Abilities Test™_ (most commonly known as the _CogAT®_) is designed to evaluate the level and pattern of cognitive development of students in grades K through 12. It is important to note that the _CogAT®_ measures developed abilities, not innate abilities. The development of these abilities begins at birth and continues through early adulthood and is vastly influenced by both in-school and out-of-school life experiences. Because these abilities are closely related to an individual's success in school, test results may be used in combination with other relevant information about a student to adapt instruction in ways that enhance the student's chances of successful learning as well as to help identify children who may belong in Gifted and Talented programs.

The _CogAT®_ is based on concepts drawn from several theoretical models of human abilities, but is based on primarily Vernon's (1961) hierarchical model and Cattell's (1987) fluid-crystallized model. In brief, both models have the factor G, or general reasoning ability, and consider it as the essential organizing cognitive construct that plays a central role in all learning and problem solving. In _CogAT®_, G is operationally defined as abstract reasoning skills with special emphasis on inductive reasoning that is fundamental for acquiring knowledge, organizing it, and storing it in memory. Vernon's and Cattell's models also provide four major group factors which Vernon calls verbal educational abilities and Cattell calls crystallized abilities. In the _CogAT®_, the Verbal and Quantitative batteries appraise some of the abilities in these clusters. The clusters become much more differentiated and more closely related to specific kinds of learning tasks as a student's age and grade in school increase.

The _CogAT®_ test measures both general and specific reasoning abilities. The general reasoning abilities reflect the overall efficiency of cognitive processes and strategies that enable individuals to learn new tasks and solve problems in the absence of direct instruction. These abilities are assessed in three domains: verbal, quantitative, and nonverbal. Each domain is represented by two or three different reasoning tasks to ensure the dependability of the score that is reported for each student.

*CogAT*® **Practice Test Level 8 - Instructions**

Bright Kids NYC Inc ©

## *CogAT®* Form 7 Content and Format

*The Cognitive Abilities Test* (*CogAT®*) is designed primarily for use in schools in order to evaluate general cognitive abilities that are fundamental to achieving instructional objectives at each grade. Since the primary purpose of *CogAT®* is to provide a description of the levels and kinds of cognitive resources that a student has for learning, separate batteries appraise general cognitive skills using verbal, quantitative, and nonverbal test tasks. *CogAT®*7 has been updated from the *CogAT®*6 to reduce the oral vocabulary portion in order to reduce the bias towards children who are new English learners.

Each battery of the *CogAT®* uses a variety of test tasks such as verbal classification, sentence completion, and verbal analogies. These tasks were selected because research has demonstrated that they are valid measures of abstract reasoning skills.

All nine subtests from the Multilevel Battery, which are administered in grades three through twelve, now extend to the Primary Battery grades, which are kindergarten through second grade. On Form 7, only one of the three tests on the Verbal Battery, the Sentence Completion Subtest, and none of the items on the three Quantitative tests require comprehension of oral language, making the test more accessible and valid for new English learners. Items used on the new primary-level tests were selected from a larger pool of items that were designed to remove language bias for new English learners. Finally, the total testing time is slightly less compared to previous editions.

The Primary Edition 7, which consists of Levels 5/6, 7, and 8, is designed for students in kindergarten through second grade. The Verbal Battery has 42, 48, or 54 items, at Levels 5/6, 7, and 8, respectively. The Quantitative and Nonverbal Battery have 38, 44, or 50 items, at Levels 5/6, 7, and 8, respectively. The items in each battery are divided into three subtests that have different formats. All directions are read aloud by an examiner, who also paces students through the questions. The structure and format of the Primary Edition test items have been altered to create more consistency with the Multilevel Edition.

The Multilevel Edition of Form 7, which includes Levels 9 through 17/18, is designed for students in grades three through twelve. Level 9 is the transition point where the test shifts from picture-based, examiner-paced verbal and quantitative tests to the text and numeric-based, timed verbal and quantitative tests utilized at the upper grades. The Level 10 to 17/18 Verbal (64 items), Quantitative (52 items), and Nonverbal batteries (60 items) each contain three subtests that use different item formats. The student must read individual words on two subtests of the Verbal Battery (Verbal Analogies and Verbal Classification) and a sentence on the third (Sentence Completion). The three subtests of the Quantitative Battery are Number Series, Number Analogies, and Number Puzzles. The latter requires students to determine the value of variables in number sentences, i.e. complete solving equations by identifying the missing variable.

The three subtests of the Nonverbal Battery are Figure Classification, Figure Analogies, and Paper Folding, which were all described above for the level 5/6, 7, and 8 tests.

The *CogAT®* subtests are constructed in a modular format. Easy items are dropped and more difficult items are added as one moves across levels. The abstract reasoning skills appraised by each level are those that enable the student to acquire, organize, and remember information, to make inferences and detect relationships, to comprehend and analyze problem situations, to form concepts, to discover and remember sequences, to recognize patterns, to classify or categorize objects, events, and concepts, to infer rules and principles, and to relate previous experience to new learning tasks and problems.

## *CogAT®* Form 7 Subtest Descriptions

### Verbal Battery

The Verbal Battery consists of Picture Analogies, Sentence Completion and Picture Classification. In **Picture Analogies**, a two by two matrix with three pictures and an empty cell is presented in each question. Children need to figure out how the pictures in the top two boxes are related and then apply the same relationship to the pictures in the bottom row to find out what goes in the empty cell. In **Sentence Completion**, children must listen to a sentence that is read to them and then select the picture that correctly answers the question. In **Picture Classifications**, children are given three or four pictures of similar items. Then they must choose another item that would belong in the same group.

### Quantitative Battery

The Quantitative Battery consists of Number Analogies, Number Puzzles, and Number Series. In **Number Analogies** children must follow the same process as in picture analogies. The difference is that quantitative concepts such as more or less are used instead of verbal concepts. In **Number Puzzles**, each student is presented with an equation with a number missing. Children must choose the number that belongs in the empty box to make one side of the equal sign total the same amount as the other side of the equal sign. In **Number Series**, each question represents a series of beads on an abacus. The beads create a pattern and children must find the next set of beads that will complete the pattern.

### Nonverbal Battery

The Nonverbal Battery consists of Figure Matrices, Paper Folding and Figure Classifications. In **Figure Matrices**, children must follow the same process as in Picture and Number Analogies, but instead of pictures, the questions utilize figural shapes to test spatial skills. **In Paper Folding**, students must visualize what happens when a piece of paper is folded and cut in some way and then unfolded. In **Figure Classifications**, children will be presented three or four figures or geometric shapes and then select a figure that belongs in the same set.

TABLE 1: Distribution of Types of Questions [1]

| SUBTEST | Level 5/6 | Level 7 | Level 8 | Level 9 | Levels 10 -17/18 |
|---|---|---|---|---|---|
| **Grade** | K | 1st | 2nd | 3rd | 4th to 11th |
| **Verbal Battery** | | | | | |
| Picture/Verbal Analogies | 14 | 16 | 18 | 22 | 24 |
| Sentence Completion | 14 | 16 | 18 | 20 | 20 |
| Picture/Verbal Classifications | 14 | 16 | 18 | 20 | 20 |
| **Quantitative Battery** | | | | | |
| Number Analogies | 14 | 16 | 18 | 18 | 18 |
| Number Puzzles | 10 | 12 | 14 | 16 | 16 |
| Number Series | 14 | 16 | 18 | 18 | 18 |
| **Nonverbal Battery** | | | | | |
| Figure Matrices | 14 | 16 | 18 | 20 | 22 |
| Paper Folding | 10 | 12 | 16 | 16 | 16 |
| Figure Classification | 14 | 16 | 18 | 20 | 22 |
| **Total** | **118** | **136** | **156** | **170** | **176** |

---

[1]This may or may not represent the question mix of the actual *CogAT®* test, as the mix among different types of questions may change from test to test.

## Scoring Guidelines

*CogAT®* test results provide a wealth of useful information. The scores can be used as follows:

1) To create individualized instruction: Each student gets a score report that includes stanines, relative strengths and weaknesses, as well as extreme score differences.

2) To identify gifted students: The high ceiling on the *CogAT®* allows for reliable discrimination among the top 10 percent of scores in all age groups.

3) To predict achievement: The *CogAT®* has been normed with the Iowa Test of Basic Skills® (ITBS®) and the Iowa Tests of Educational Development®. The joint norming of *CogAT®* with elementary and secondary school achievement tests allows for predicting likely achievement levels of students tested with *CogAT®*.

4) To identify at-risk students.

5) To evaluate current and new curricula.

Each child receives a composite or a total score on the *CogAT®* as well as a stanine or a percentile rank. The composite or total score indicates the overall strength of the student's cognitive resources for learning. As the level of the composite score decreases, the variety and strength of the student's cognitive resources also decrease and the need for help with learning increases. Students with an above-average or very high composite score have an array of strongly developed cognitive resources. They usually learn quickly and typically need no special help to achieve instructional objectives. Students with a below-average or very low composite score have very few and very weak cognitive resources, typically learn very slowly, and need considerable assistance to achieve instructional objectives.

The Bright Kids *CogAT®* Practice Test can be scored only based on the total number of correct answers, or the overall raw score. Since this practice test has not been standardized with the *CogAT®*, scaled scores, stanines, or percentile ranks cannot be obtained from the raw score. Please realize that a child can miss many questions on the test and still obtain a high score. Thus, it is important that this practice test is utilized as a learning tool to help evaluate a child's strengths and weaknesses rather than to estimate a stanine or a percentile rank.

## General Administration Guidelines

The test is typically administered in two or three different sittings. There is a short rest period recommended if two subtests are administered in one sitting.

Since the test is designed to measure how well, rather than how fast, students solve problems, there is no specific time limit for each part. The time allocations are shown to determine how much time may be needed to complete the test.

The recommended timeline is as follows:

**First Sitting**

| | |
|---|---|
| *Distributing Materials & Practice Questions* | *Approximately 5 minutes* |
| Test 1: Picture Analogies | Approximately 15 minutes |
| Test 2: Sentence Completion | Approximately 15 minutes |
| Test 3: Picture Classification | Approximately 15 minutes |

**Second Sitting**

| | |
|---|---|
| *Distributing Materials & Practice Questions* | *Approximately 5 minutes* |
| Test 4: Number Analogies | Approximately 13 minutes |
| Test 5: Number Puzzles | Approximately 11 minutes |
| Test 6: Number Series | Approximately 15 minutes |

**Third Sitting**

| | |
|---|---|
| *Distributing Materials & Practice Questions* | *Approximately 5 minutes* |
| Test 7: Figure Matrices | Approximately 11 minutes |
| Test 8: Paper Folding | Approximately 10 minutes |
| Test 9: Figure Classification | Approximately 10 minutes |

**CogAT® Practice Test Level 8 - Instructions** Bright Kids NYC Inc ©

# Getting Ready

## Materials

1. Several No. 2 soft lead pencils, erasers, and pencil sharpeners.

2. Ideally, a "Do Not Disturb" sign for the room where you will be administering the test.

3. Questions booklet.

## Prior to Testing

1. Familiarize yourself with the test and the instructions. Take the actual test to make sure that you can later explain to the child why certain answers are correct or incorrect.

2. Provide satisfactory physical conditions in the room where the child will be taking the test. Make sure that there is ample lighting and ventilation.

3. To prevent interruptions, give the child the test when there are no other distractions in the house. If the house is not suitable, try to find a local library or a school.

## During Testing

1. Make sure that the child knows how to accurately mark the answers. Help the child as needed by utilizing the sample questions.

2. Read all instructions exactly as they are written; do not paraphrase or change the questions.

3. Pace the test and utilize the breaks as needed.

4. Do not give the child any feedback during testing. Discuss the answers only after the testing is complete.

4. Always provide positive reinforcements to ensure that the child completes the task.

*CogAT*® Practice Test Level 8 - Instructions

# Bright Kids NYC
# *CogAT*® Practice Test

## Instructions

### Level 8

### Second Grade

*CogAT*® **Practice Test Level 8 - Instructions**

# Test One:
# Picture Analogies

**_CogAT_® Practice Test Level 8 - Instructions** Bright Kids NYC Inc ©

## Test One – Picture Analogies

SAY: **Today, we are going to do some fun activities in the booklet in front of you. Please keep your booklet closed until I ask you to open it.**

SAMPLE ONE

SAY: **Now open your booklet and look at the first page. Look at the sample question.**

SAY: **Listen. Here, you will see four boxes. Look at the first row. In the first box on top there is a piece of paper. In the box next to the piece of paper, there is a pair of scissors. These top two boxes go together in a certain way. Now look at the first box on the bottom, where there is a piece of wood. The other box next to it is empty. Now look at the row of three pictures next to the four boxes and find what should be in the empty box. What do you think goes with wood, the same way that a piece of paper goes with a pair of scissors?**

Pause and let the child answer.

SAY: **Did you find the answer?**

SAY: **You are right. The correct answer is the second one, a saw. You cut a piece of paper with a pair of scissors and you cut a piece of wood with a saw. Great job!**

SAY: **Now fill in the circle under the saw. Simply color in the circle completely using your pencil. Try to fill in the circle as best as you can.**

Demonstrate how to fill in an answer if the child seems confused. Remind the child that it does not have to be perfect, but circles must be visibly filled. Also let the child know that he or she can bubble only one answer choice.

Make sure the child understands the sample question above before moving on to the test questions.

SAY: **On the next few pages, we will be doing more activities like this. I will tell you which question and row to work on. Do the best that you can with each picture and do not worry if you are not sure of all of the answers. Be sure to bubble in the whole answer space each time you mark your answer. If you want to change an answer, erase all of your first mark and mark the new answer.**

SAY: **Now move to the next page and look at the first row and the first question.**

1. **Look at question number one. Look at the pictures. Fill in the circle under the picture that goes in the empty box with the question mark.**

2. **Look at question number two. Look at the pictures. Fill in the circle under the picture that goes in the empty box with the question mark.**

3. **Look at question number three. Look at the pictures. Fill in the circle under the picture that goes in the empty box with the question mark.**

SAY: **Turn to the next page and look at the first row.**

4. **Look at question number four. Look at the pictures. Fill in the circle under the picture that goes in the empty box with the question mark.**

5. **Look at question number five. Look at the pictures. Fill in the circle under the picture that goes in the empty box with the question mark.**

6. **Look at question number six. Look at the pictures. Fill in the circle under the picture that goes in the empty box with the question mark.**

SAY: **Turn to the next page and look at the first row.**

7. **Look at question number seven. Look at the pictures. Fill in the circle under the picture that goes in the empty box with the question mark.**

8. **Look at question number eight. Look at the pictures. Fill in the circle under the picture that goes in the empty box with the question mark.**

9. **Look at question number nine. Look at the pictures. Fill in the circle under the picture that goes in the empty box with the question mark.**

SAY: **Turn to the next page and look at the first row.**

10. **Look at question number ten. Look at the pictures. Fill in the circle under the picture that goes in the empty box with the question mark.**

11. **Look at question number eleven. Look at the pictures. Fill in the circle under the picture that goes in the empty box with the question mark.**

12. **Look at question number twelve. Look at the pictures. Fill in the circle under the picture that goes in the empty box with the question mark.**

SAY: **Turn the page to the next page and look at the first row.**

13. **Look at question number thirteen. Look at the pictures. Fill in the circle under the picture that goes in the empty box with the question mark.**

14. **Look at question number fourteen. Look at the pictures. Fill in the circle under the picture that goes in the empty box with the question mark.**

15. **Look at question number fifteen. Look at the pictures. Fill in the circle under the picture that goes in the empty box with the question mark.**

SAY: **Turn the page to the next page and look at the first row.**

16. **Look at question number sixteen. Look at the pictures. Fill in the circle under the picture that goes in the empty box with the question mark.**

17. **Look at question number seventeen. Look at the pictures. Fill in the circle under the picture that goes in the empty box with the question mark.**

18. **Look at question number eighteen. Look at the pictures. Fill in the circle under the picture that goes in the empty box with the question mark.**

*CogAT*® **Practice Test Level 8 - Instructions**

# Test Two:
# Sentence Completion

**CogAT® Practice Test Level 8 - Instructions**

Bright Kids NYC Inc ©

## Test Two – Sentence Completion

SAY: **The questions on this test are like the practice question that we will do together. Listen carefully.**

SAMPLE ONE

SAY: **Look at the pictures on the page. Listen. What would you use to take pictures with? Fill in the circle under the right answer.**

Pause and wait until the child answers the question.

SAY: **You should have filled in the circle under the first answer, the picture of a camera. If you chose another answer, erase it and fill in the circle under the first picture, the camera.**

SAY: **On the next few pages, we will be doing more activities like this. I will tell you which question and row to work on. Do the best that you can with each picture and do not worry if you are not sure of all of the answers. Be sure to bubble in the whole answer space each time you mark your answer. If you want to change an answer, erase all of your first mark and mark the new answer.**

SAY: **Now turn to the next page.**

1. **Look at question number one. Which item makes things look bigger? Fill in the circle under the right answer.**

2. **Look at question number two. Which child is dozing? Fill in the circle under the right answer.**

3. **Look at question number three. Which will protect you from the sun? Fill in the circle under the right answer.**

SAY: **Move to the next page.**

4. **Look at question number four. What activity would you do when you are not tired? Fill in the circle under the right answer.**

5. **Look at question number five. Which one measures in pounds? Fill in the circle under the right answer.**

6. **Look at question number six. What animal slithers? Fill in the circle under the right answer.**

SAY: **Move to the next page.**

7. Look at question number seven. Michaela wanted to make muffins. What item would she NOT need? Fill in the circle under the right answer.

8. Look at question number eight. John remembered his hat but forgot his shoes and socks at home. Which one is John? Fill in the circle under the right answer.

9. Look at question number nine. Which item is fragile? Fill in the circle under the right answer.

SAY: **Move to the next page.**

10. Look at question number ten. Which animal does NOT live in a cold place? Fill in the circle under the right answer.

11. Look at question number eleven. Which item would not work on the beach? Fill in the circle under the right answer.

12. Look at question number twelve. Calvin's shirt is blue with white stripes. Frank's is just the opposite. Which shirt is Frank's? Fill in the circle under the right answer.

SAY: **Move to the next page.**

13. Look at question number thirteen. Which animal does not always live in the water? Fill in the circle under the right answer.

14. Look at question number fourteen. What can be folded? Fill in the circle under the right answer.

15. Look at question number fifteen. What item will NOT sink? Fill in the circle under the right answer.

SAY: **Move to the next page.**

16. Look at question number sixteen. Which one shows a roadblock? Fill in the circle under the right answer.

17. Look at question number seventeen. What would you wear on your head for safety? Fill in the circle under the right answer.

18. Look at question number eighteen. Which child is doing chores? Fill in the circle under the right answer.

# Test Three:
# Picture Classification

## Test Three – Picture Classification

SAY: **The questions on this test are like the practice question that we will do together. Listen carefully.**

SAMPLE ONE

SAY: **Look at the pictures on the page. Listen. Here, you see some pictures that go across. When pictures go across, they are said to be in a row. In the top row, there are three pictures that are similar in some way. In the bottom row, there are three other pictures. Find the picture in the bottom row that is similar to the three pictures in the top row.**

Pause and wait until the child answers the question.

SAY: **You should have filled in the circle under the first answer, the picture of a cube. In the top row, there are three different kinds of three-dimensional shapes. The only other picture that is similar to the top pictures is another three-dimensional shape, which is a cube. If you chose another answer, erase it and fill in the circle under the first picture.**

SAY: **Do you understand what we just did?**

SAY: **On the next few pages, we will be doing more activities like this. I will tell you which question and row to work on. Do the best that you can with each picture and do not worry if you are not sure of all of the answers. Be sure to bubble in the whole answer space each time you mark your answer. If you want to change an answer, erase all of your first mark and mark the new answer.**

SAY: **Now turn the page and look at the first row.**

1. **Look at question number one. Find the picture from the bottom row that is the most similar to the three pictures in the top row. Fill in the circle under the right answer.**

2. **Look at question number two. Find the picture from the bottom row that is the most similar to the three pictures in the top row. Fill in the circle under the right answer.**

3. **Look at question number three. Find the picture from the bottom row that is the most similar to the three pictures in the top row. Fill in the circle under the right answer.**

SAY: **Now turn the page and look at the first row.**

4. Look at question number four. Find the picture from the bottom row that is the most similar to the three pictures in the top row. Fill in the circle under the right answer.

5. Look at question number five. Find the picture from the bottom row that is the most similar to the three pictures in the top row. Fill in the circle under the right answer.

6. Look at question number six. Find the picture from the bottom row that is the most similar to the three pictures in the top row. Fill in the circle under the right answer.

SAY: **Now turn the page.**

7. Look at question number seven. Find the picture from the bottom row that is the most similar to the three pictures in the top row. Fill in the circle under the right answer.

8. Look at question number eight. Find the picture from the bottom row that is the most similar to the three pictures in the top row. Fill in the circle under the right answer.

9. Look at question number nine. Find the picture from the bottom row that is the most similar to the three pictures in the top row.

SAY: **Now turn the page.**

10. Look at question number ten. Find the picture from the bottom row that is the most similar to the three pictures in the top row. Fill in the circle under the right answer.

11. Look at question number eleven. Find the picture from the bottom row that is the most similar to the three pictures in the top row. Fill in the circle under the right answer.

12. Look at question number twelve. Find the picture from the bottom row that is the most similar to the three pictures in the top row. Fill in the circle under the right answer.

SAY: **Now turn the page.**

13. Look at question number thirteen. Find the picture from the bottom row that is the most similar to the three pictures in the top row. Fill in the circle under the right answer.

14. **Look at question number fourteen. Find the picture from the bottom row that is the most similar to the three pictures in the top row. Fill in the circle under the right answer.**

15. **Look at question number fifteen. Find the picture from the bottom row that is the most similar to the three pictures in the top row. Fill in the circle under the right answer.**

SAY: **Now turn the page.**

16. **Look at question number sixteen. Find the picture from the bottom row that is the most similar to the three pictures in the top row. Fill in the circle under the right answer.**

17. **Look at question number seventeen. Find the picture from the bottom row that is the most similar to the three pictures in the top row. Fill in the circle under the right answer.**

18. **Look at question number eighteen. Find the picture from the bottom row that is the most similar to the three pictures in the top row. Fill in the circle under the right answer.**

*CogAT®* **Practice Test Level 8 - Instructions**

Bright Kids NYC Inc ©

# Test Four:
# Number Analogies

## Test Four – Number Analogies

SAY: **The questions on this test are like the practice question that we will do together. Listen carefully.**

SAMPLE ONE

SAY: **Look at the first row of pictures on the page. Listen. Look at the two pictures in the two boxes on the top. These two pictures go together in a certain way. In the first box on top, there is an apple. Inside the second box, there is half an apple. Now look at the picture inside the first box on the bottom. There is a loaf of bread. What do you think belongs in the empty box? Can you mark under the picture that belongs in the empty box?**

Pause and wait until the child selects an answer.

SAY: **You should have marked the first choice that has a half a loaf of bread. The first picture goes from one apple to half an apple, and the loaf of bread should go from a whole loaf of bread to half a loaf of bread. If you chose another answer, erase it and fill in the circle under the first picture. Do you understand what we just did?**

Answer any questions the child may have.

SAY: **On the next few pages, we will be doing more activities like this. I will tell you which question and row to work on. Do the best that you can with each picture and do not worry if you are not sure of all of the answers. Be sure to bubble in the whole answer space each time you mark your answer. If you want to change an answer, erase all of your first mark and mark the new answer.**

SAY: **Now turn the page.**

1. **Look at question number one. Find the picture that belongs in the empty box. Fill in the circle under the correct answer.**

2. **Look at question number two. Find the picture that belongs in the empty box. Fill in the circle under the correct answer.**

3. **Look at question number three. Find the picture that belongs in the empty box. Fill in the circle under the correct answer.**

SAY: **Now turn the page.**

4. **Look at question number four. Find the picture that belongs in the empty box. Fill in the circle under the correct answer.**

5. **Look at question number five. Find the picture that belongs in the empty box. Fill in the circle under the correct answer.**

6. **Look at question number six. Find the picture that belongs in the empty box. Fill in the circle under the correct answer.**

SAY: **Now turn the page.**

7. **Look at question number seven. Find the picture that belongs in the empty box. Fill in the circle under the correct answer.**

8. **Look at question number eight. Find the picture that belongs in the empty box. Fill in the circle under the correct answer.**

9. **Look at question number nine. Find the picture that belongs in the empty box. Fill in the circle under the correct answer.**

SAY: **Now turn the page.**

10. **Look at question number ten. Find the picture that belongs in the empty box. Fill in the circle under the correct answer.**

11. **Look at question number eleven. Find the picture that belongs in the empty box. Fill in the circle under the correct answer.**

12. **Look at question number twelve. Find the picture that belongs in the empty box. Fill in the circle under the correct answer.**

SAY: **Now turn the page.**

13. **Look at question number thirteen. Find the picture that belongs in the empty box. Fill in the circle under the correct answer.**

14. **Look at question number fourteen. Find the picture that belongs in the empty box. Fill in the circle under the correct answer.**

15. **Look at question number fifteen. Find the picture that belongs in the empty box. Fill in the circle under the correct answer.**

SAY: **Now turn the page.**

16. **Look at question number sixteen. Find the picture that belongs in the empty box. Fill in the circle under the correct answer.**

17. **Look at question number seventeen. Find the picture that belongs in the empty box. Fill in the circle under the correct answer.**

18. **Look at question number eighteen. Find the picture that belongs in the empty box. Fill in the circle under the correct answer.**

# Test Five:
# Number Puzzles

*CogAT*® **Practice Test Level 8 - Instructions**

## Test Five – Number Puzzles

SAY: **The questions on this test are like the practice questions that we will do together. Listen carefully.**

SAMPLE ONE

SAY: **Look at the numbers in the boxes. The question is asking you: 5 = 7 – what number? You need to find what number can be subtracted from seven to equal five. Look at all the answer choices and fill in the circle under the correct answer.**

Pause and wait until the child selects an answer.

SAY: **You should have marked the third answer choice, the number 2. When we subtract 2 from 7, the numbers on both sides of the equal sign total 5. Do you understand what we just did?**

Answer any questions the child may have.

SAMPLE TWO

SAY: **Let's answer another practice question. What number goes in the empty box to make both sides equal eight? Look at all the answer choices and fill in the circle under the correct answer.**

Pause and wait until the child selects an answer.

SAY: **You should have marked the second answer, the number 3. In this puzzle, we need to find what number goes in the empty box so that both sides of the equal sign total eight. 4 + 1 is 5, so we need to add 3 to make both sides of the equal sign total 8. Do you understand what we just did?**

Answer any questions the child may have.

SAY: **On the next few pages, we will be doing more activities like these. I will tell you which question and row to work on. Do the best that you can with each picture and do not worry if you are not sure of all of the answers. Be sure to bubble in the whole answer space each time you mark your answer. If you want to change an answer, erase all of your first mark and mark the new answer.**

SAY: **Turn to the next page.**

1. Look at question number one. Find the number that goes in the empty box to make both sides of the equal sign total the same amount. Fill in the circle under the correct answer.

2. Look at question number two. Find the number that goes in the empty box to make both sides of the equal sign total the same amount. Fill in the circle under the correct answer.

3. Look at question number three. Find the number that goes in the empty box to make both sides of the equal sign total the same amount. Fill in the circle under the correct answer.

SAY: **Turn to the next page.**

4. Look at question number four. Find the number that goes in the empty box to make both sides of the equal sign total the same amount. Fill in the circle under the correct answer.

5. Look at question number five. Find the number that goes in the empty box to make both sides of the equal sign total the same amount. Fill in the circle under the correct answer.

6. Look at question number six. Find the number that goes in the empty box to make both sides of the equal sign total the same amount. Fill in the circle under the correct answer.

SAY: **Turn to the next page.**

7. Look at question number seven. Find the number that goes in the empty box to make both sides of the equal sign total the same amount. Fill in the circle under the correct answer.

8. Look at question number eight. Find the number that goes in the empty box to make both sides of the equal sign total the same amount. Fill in the circle under the correct answer.

9. Look at question number nine. Find the number that goes in the empty box to make both sides of the equal sign total the same amount. Fill in the circle under the correct answer.

SAY: **Turn to the next page.**

10. Look at question number ten. Find the number that goes in the empty box to make both sides of the equal sign total the same amount. Fill in the circle under the correct answer.

11. **Look at question number eleven. Find the number that goes in the empty box to make both sides of the equal sign total the same amount. Fill in the circle under the correct answer.**

12. **Look at question number twelve. Find the number that goes in the empty box to make both sides of the equal sign total the same amount. Fill in the circle under the correct answer.**

SAY: **Turn to the next page.**

13. **Look at question number thirteen. Find the number that goes in the empty box to make both sides of the equal sign total the same amount. Fill in the circle under the correct answer.**

14. **Look at question number fourteen. Find the number that goes in the empty box to make both sides of the equal sign total the same amount. Fill in the circle under the correct answer.**

*CogAT*® **Practice Test Level 8 - Instructions** Bright Kids NYC Inc ©

# Test Six:
# Number Series

**CogAT® Practice Test Level 8 - Instructions** Bright Kids NYC Inc ©

## Test Six – Number Series

SAY: **The questions on this test are like the practice questions that we will do together. Listen carefully.**

<u>SAMPLE ONE</u>

SAY: **Look at the first sample question. Look at the abacus. There are four rods in the abacus, and the last rod has a question mark and has missing beads. Look for a pattern or an underlying rule of the beads on the first three rods to determine which rod comes next that will have the correct number of beads. Look at all the answer choices and fill in the circle under the correct answer.**

Pause and wait until the child selects an answer.

SAY: **You should have marked the second answer that has four beads. The rule is that the beads are increasing by one. The first rod has one bead, the second one has two beads, and the third one has three beads. So, the fourth one must have four beads. Do you understand what we just did?**

Answer any questions the child may have.

<u>SAMPLE TWO</u>

SAY: **Move to the second sample question. Look at the abacus. There are seven rods in the abacus, and the last rod has a question mark and has missing beads. Look for a pattern or an underlying rule of the beads on the first six rods to determine which rod comes next that will have the correct number of beads. Look at all the answer choices and fill in the circle under the correct answer.**

Pause and wait until the child selects an answer.

SAY: **You should have marked the third answer that has eight beads. Again, the rule is that the beads are increasing by one. You have to look carefully at the answer choices to pick the rod with the correct number of beads. Do you understand what we just did?**

Answer any questions the child may have.

SAY: **On the next few pages, we will be doing more activities like these. I will tell you which question and row to work on. Do the best that you can with each picture and do not worry if you are not sure of all of the answers. Be sure to bubble in the whole answer space each time you mark your answer. If you want to change an answer, erase all of your first mark and mark the new answer.**

SAY: **Turn to the next page.**

1. **Look at question number one. Find the abacus rod that has the correct number of missing beads. Fill in the circle under the correct answer.**

2. **Look at question number two. Find the abacus rod that has the correct number of missing beads. Fill in the circle under the correct answer.**

3. **Look at question number three. Find the abacus rod that has the correct number of missing beads. Fill in the circle under the correct answer.**

SAY: **Turn to the next page.**

4. **Look at question number four. Find the abacus rod that has the correct number of missing beads. Fill in the circle under the correct answer.**

5. **Look at question number five. Find the abacus rod that has the correct number of missing beads. Fill in the circle under the correct answer.**

6. **Look at question number six. Find the abacus rod that has the correct number of missing beads. Fill in the circle under the correct answer.**

SAY: **Turn to the next page.**

7. **Look at question number seven. Find the abacus rod that has the correct number of missing beads. Fill in the circle under the correct answer.**

8. **Look at question number eight. Find the abacus rod that has the correct number of missing beads. Fill in the circle under the correct answer.**

9. **Look at question number nine. Find the abacus rod that has the correct number of missing beads. Fill in the circle under the correct answer.**

SAY: **Turn to the next page.**

10. **Look at question number ten. Find the abacus rod that has the correct number of missing beads. Fill in the circle under the correct answer.**

11. **Look at question number eleven. Find the abacus rod that has the correct number of missing beads. Fill in the circle under the correct answer.**

12. **Look at question number twelve. Find the abacus rod that has the correct number of missing beads. Fill in the circle under the correct answer.**

SAY: **Turn to the next page.**

13. **Look at question number thirteen. Find the abacus rod that has the correct number of missing beads. Fill in the circle under the correct answer.**

14. **Look at question number fourteen. Find the abacus rod that has the correct number of missing beads. Fill in the circle under the correct answer.**

15. **Look at question number fifteen. Find the abacus rod that has the correct number of missing beads. Fill in the circle under the correct answer.**

SAY: **Turn to the next page.**

16. **Look at question number sixteen. Find the abacus rod that has the correct number of missing beads. Fill in the circle under the correct answer.**

17. **Look at question number seventeen. Find the abacus rod that has the correct number of missing beads. Fill in the circle under the correct answer.**

18. **Look at question number eighteen. Find the abacus rod that has the correct number of missing beads. Fill in the circle under the correct answer.**

CogAT® Practice Test Level 8 - Instructions

# Test Seven:
# Figure Matrices

**CogAT® Practice Test Level 8 - Instructions**     Bright Kids NYC Inc ©

## Test Seven – Figure Matrices

SAY: **The questions on this test are like the practice questions that we will do together. Listen carefully.**

SAMPLE ONE

SAY: **Look at the first sample question. Listen. The four boxes are like a puzzle, with a piece missing from it. The first box on the top has a yellow square inside. The second box on the top also has a yellow square inside, but a smaller one. In this puzzle, the two boxes in the first row must have the same shape in them, but the shape must get smaller. Look at the bottom row. The first box has a yellow circle inside. Now, solve the puzzle by finding out what will go in the second box in the bottom row.**

Pause and wait until the child answers the question.

SAY: **You should have filled in the circle under the third answer, the picture of a small yellow circle. If you chose another answer, erase it and fill in the circle under the third picture. Do you understand what we just did?**

Answer any questions the child may have.

SAMPLE TWO

SAY: **Now look at the second sample question. The first box has a small green square on top of a big green square. The second box in the top row has a big green square on top of a small green square. In other words, the figure has been flipped. Look at the bottom row. The first box has a big purple square on top of a small purple square. Now, solve the puzzle by finding out what will go in the second box in the bottom row.**

Pause and wait until the child answers the question.

SAY: **You should have filled in the circle under the second answer, the picture of a small purple square on top of a big purple square. If you chose another answer, erase it and fill in the circle under the second picture. Any questions?**

Answer any questions the child may have.

SAY: **On the next few pages, we will be doing more activities like these. I will tell you which question and row to work on. Do the best that you can with each picture and do not worry if you are not sure of all of the answers. Be sure to bubble in the whole answer space each time you mark your answer. If you want to change an answer, erase all of your first mark and mark the new answer.**

SAY: **Turn to the next page.**

1. **Look at question number one. Find the shape that belongs in the empty box. Fill in the circle under the correct answer.**

2. **Look at question number two. Find the shape that belongs in the empty box. Fill in the circle under the correct answer.**

3. **Look at question number three. Find the shape that belongs in the empty box. Fill in the circle under the correct answer.**

SAY: **Turn to the next page.**

4. **Look at question number four. Find the shape that belongs in the empty box. Fill in the circle under the correct answer.**

5. **Look at question number five. Find the shape that belongs in the empty box. Fill in the circle under the correct answer.**

6. **Look at question number six. Find the shape that belongs in the empty box. Fill in the circle under the correct answer.**

SAY: **Turn to the next page.**

7. **Look at question number seven. Find the shape that belongs in the empty box. Fill in the circle under the correct answer.**

8. **Look at question number eight. Find the shape that belongs in the empty box. Fill in the circle under the correct answer.**

9. **Look at question number nine. Find the shape that belongs in the empty box. Fill in the circle under the correct answer.**

SAY: **Turn to the next page.**

10. **Look at question number ten. Find the shape that belongs in the empty box. Fill in the circle under the correct answer.**

11. **Look at question number eleven. Find the shape that belongs in the empty box. Fill in the circle under the correct answer.**

12. **Look at question number twelve. Find the shape that belongs in the empty box. Fill in the circle under the correct answer.**

SAY: **Turn to the next page.**

13. **Look at question number thirteen. Find the shape that belongs in the empty box. Fill in the circle under the correct answer.**

14. **Look at question number fourteen. Find the shape that belongs in the empty box. Fill in the circle under the correct answer.**

15. **Look at question number fifteen. Find the shape that belongs in the empty box. Fill in the circle under the correct answer.**

SAY: **Turn to the next page.**

16. **Look at question number sixteen. Find the shape that belongs in the empty box. Fill in the circle under the correct answer.**

17. **Look at question number seventeen. Find the shape that belongs in the empty box. Fill in the circle under the correct answer.**

18. **Look at question number eighteen. Find the shape that belongs in the empty box. Fill in the circle under the correct answer.**

# Test Eight:
# Paper Folding

**CogAT® Practice Test Level 8 - Instructions**

## Test Eight – Paper Folding

SAY: **The questions on this test are like the practice questions that we will do together. Listen carefully.**

<u>SAMPLE ONE</u>

SAY: **Look at the first sample question. Each question has a piece of paper that is folded. The objective is to find out what the paper will look like when it is unfolded.**

SAY: **Look at the top row, first picture. It shows the way the paper looks before it is folded. The arrow shows the direction of the fold, and the dotted line shows where the paper will be folded. Now let's see what happens to the paper. Look at the second picture. Here the paper is folded a little. Then, it is folded more, as seen in the third picture. Finally, the fourth picture shows the paper folded in half.**

Pause and see if the child has any questions.

SAY: **Finally, look at the answer choices below. The objective is to determine what the paper will look like, when it is unfolded. The correct answer is the first choice, since this picture looks like the same diamond paper we started with. Do you understand what we just did?**

Answer any questions the child may have.

<u>SAMPLE TWO</u>

SAY: **Move to the second sample question. The objective is to find out how the paper will look when it is unfolded.**

SAY: **Look at the top row, first picture. It shows the way the paper looks before it is folded. The arrow shows the direction of the fold, and the dotted line shows where the paper will be folded. In this example, the paper will be folded in half from left to right.**

SAY: **Next, look at the last picture in this row. The last picture shows what the paper looks like after a hole has been punched through the folded paper. The dotted lines show the paper size, prior to folding. The white circle shows where the paper has been punched.**

SAY: **Finally, look at the answer choices below. The objective is to find what the paper will now look like when it is unfolded. Please note that a hole has been punched through the folded paper, through two layers. Thus, there must be two** holes in the paper when it is unfolded. Since the paper was folded in half, from left to right, the holes must be a mirror image of one another. Thus, one hole must be to the far right and another to the far left.

Pause and see if the child has any questions.

SAY: **The correct answer is the first choice, since this paper has one hole on the right side and another on the left side, opposite of each other. Do you understand what we just did?**

Answer any questions the child may have.

SAY: **On the next few pages, we will be doing more activities like these. I will tell you which question and row to work on. Do the best that you can with each picture and do not worry if you are not sure of all of the answers. Be sure to bubble in the whole answer space each time you mark your answer. If you want to change an answer, erase all of your first mark and mark the new answer.**

SAY: **Turn to the next page.**

1. **Look at question number one. Look at how the paper is folded. Look at all the answer choices and find how the paper will look when it is unfolded. Fill in the circle under the correct answer.**

2. **Look at question number two. Look at how the paper is folded. Look at all the answer choices and find how the paper will look when it is unfolded. Fill in the circle under the correct answer.**

3. **Look at question number three. Look at how the paper is folded. Look at all the answer choices and find how the paper will look when it is unfolded. Fill in the circle under the correct answer.**

SAY: **Turn to the next page.**

4. **Look at question number four. Look at how the paper is folded. Look at all the answer choices and find how the paper will look when it is unfolded. Fill in the circle under the correct answer.**

5. **Look at question number five. Look at how the paper is folded. Look at all the answer choices and find how the paper will look when it is unfolded. Fill in the circle under the correct answer.**

6. **Look at question number six. Look at how the paper is folded. Look at all the answer choices and find how the paper will look when it is unfolded. Fill in the circle under the correct answer.**

SAY: **Turn to the next page.**

7. Look at question number seven. Look at how the paper is folded. Look at all the answer choices and find how the paper will look when it is unfolded. Fill in the circle under the correct answer.

8. Look at question number eight. Look at how the paper is folded. Look at all the answer choices and find how the paper will look when it is unfolded. Fill in the circle under the correct answer.

9. Look at question number nine. Look at how the paper is folded. Look at all the answer choices and find how the paper will look when it is unfolded. Fill in the circle under the correct answer.

SAY: **Turn to the next page.**

10. Look at question number ten. Look at how the paper is folded. Look at all the answer choices and find how the paper will look when it is unfolded. Fill in the circle under the correct answer.

11. Look at question number eleven. Look at how the paper is folded. Look at all the answer choices and find how the paper will look when it is unfolded. Fill in the circle under the correct answer.

12. Look at question number twelve. Look at how the paper is folded. Look at all the answer choices and find how the paper will look when it is unfolded. Fill in the circle under the correct answer.

SAY: **Turn to the next page.**

13. Look at question number thirteen. Look at how the paper is folded. Look at all the answer choices and find how the paper will look when it is unfolded. Fill in the circle under the correct answer.

14. Look at question number fourteen. Look at how the paper is folded. Look at all the answer choices and find how the paper will look when it is unfolded. Fill in the circle under the correct answer.

15. Look at question number fifteen. Look at how the paper is folded. Look at all the answer choices and find how the paper will look when it is unfolded. Fill in the circle under the correct answer.

SAY: **Turn to the next page.**

16. Look at question number sixteen. Look at how the paper is folded. Look at all the answer choices and find how the paper will look when it is unfolded. Fill in the circle under the correct answer.

# Test Nine:
# Figure Classification

*CogAT*® **Practice Test Level 8 - Instructions**    Bright Kids NYC Inc ©

## Test Nine – Figure Classification

SAY: **The questions on this test are like the practice questions that we will do together. Listen carefully.**

<u>SAMPLE ONE</u>

SAY: **Look at sample question one. Listen. Look at the shapes in this row. These three shapes are alike because they are all blue triangles. Now look at the rest of the pictures in this row, those that are on the other side of the line. One of these is like the first three shapes and goes together with them. Fill in the circle under the picture that goes with the three blue triangles.**

Pause and wait until the child answers the question.

SAY: **You should have filled in the circle under the second answer, the picture of a blue triangle pointing up. This triangle looks exactly like the other triangles at the beginning of the row. If you chose another answer, erase it and fill in the circle under the second picture. Do you understand what we just did?**

Answer any questions the child may have.

<u>SAMPLE TWO</u>

SAY: **Now look at the second question. This is a different type of question, so listen.**

SAY: **Look at the shapes in this row. These three shapes are not exactly alike, but they do have something in common. They are all purple circles, but they are different sizes. Now look at the rest of the pictures in the same row, those that are on the other side of the line. Find the picture that goes with the first three purple circles. Fill in the circle under the picture.**

SAY: **You should have filled in the circle under the second answer, the picture of another purple circle, but one that is a different size. If you chose another answer, erase it and fill in the circle under the second picture. Any questions?**

Answer any questions the child may have.

SAY: **On the next few pages, we will be doing more activities like these. I will tell you which question and row to work on. Do the best that you can with each picture and do not worry if you are not sure of all of the answers. Be sure to bubble in the whole answer space each time you mark your answer. If you want to change an answer, erase all of your first mark and mark the new answer.**

SAY: **Turn to the next page.**

1. **Look at question number one. Look at the first three shapes. Then, look at the shapes on the other side of the line. Find the shape that is most like the first three shapes. Fill in the circle under the right answer.**

2. **Look at question number two. Look at the first three shapes. Then, look at the shapes on the other side of the line. Find the shape that is most like the first three shapes. Fill in the circle under the right answer.**

3. **Look at question number three. Look at the first three shapes. Then, look at the shapes on the other side of the line. Find the shape that is most like the first three shapes. Fill in the circle under the right answer.**

SAY: **Now turn the page.**

4. **Look at question number four. Look at the first three shapes. Then, look at the shapes on the other side of the line. Find the shape that is most like the first three shapes. Fill in the circle under the right answer.**

5. **Look at question number five. Look at the first three shapes. Then, look at the shapes on the other side of the line. Find the shape that is most like the first three shapes. Fill in the circle under the right answer.**

6. **Look at question number six. Look at the first three shapes. Then, look at the shapes on the other side of the line. Find the shape that is most like the first three shapes. Fill in the circle under the right answer.**

SAY: **Now turn the page.**

7. **Look at question number seven. Look at the first three shapes. Then, look at the shapes on the other side of the line. Find the shape that is most like the first three shapes. Fill in the circle under the right answer.**

8. **Look at question number eight. Look at the first three shapes. Then, look at the shapes on the other side of the line. Find the shape that is most like the first three shapes. Fill in the circle under the right answer.**

9. **Look at question number nine. Look at the first three shapes. Then, look at the shapes on the other side of the line. Find the shape that is most like the first three shapes. Fill in the circle under the right answer.**

SAY: **Now turn the page.**

10. **Look at question number ten. Look at the first three shapes. Then, look at the shapes on the other side of the line. Find the shape that is most like the first three shapes. Fill in the circle under the right answer.**

11. **Look at question number eleven. Look at the first three shapes. Then, look at the shapes on the other side of the line. Find the shape that is most like the first three shapes. Fill in the circle under the right answer.**

12. **Look at question number twelve. Look at the first three shapes. Then, look at the shapes on the other side of the line. Find the shape that is most like the first three shapes. Fill in the circle under the right answer.**

SAY: **Now turn the page.**

13. **Look at question number thirteen. Look at the first three shapes. Then, look at the shapes on the other side of the line. Find the shape that is most like the first three shapes. Fill in the circle under the right answer.**

14. **Look at question number fourteen. Look at the first three shapes. Then, look at the shapes on the other side of the line. Find the shape that is most like the first three shapes. Fill in the circle under the right answer.**

15. **Look at question number fifteen. Look at the first three shapes. Then, look at the shapes on the other side of the line. Find the shape that is most like the first three shapes. Fill in the circle under the right answer.**

SAY: **Now turn the page.**

16. **Look at question number sixteen. Look at the first three shapes. Then, look at the shapes on the other side of the line. Find the shape that is most like the first three shapes. Fill in the circle under the right answer.**

17. **Look at question number seventeen. Look at the first three shapes. Then, look at the shapes on the other side of the line. Find the shape that is most like the first three shapes. Fill in the circle under the right answer.**

18. **Look at question number eighteen. Look at the first three shapes. Then, look at the shapes on the other side of the line. Find the shape that is most like the first three shapes. Fill in the circle under the right answer.**

*CogAT® Practice Test Level 8 - Instructions*

# Answer Key

*CogAT*® **Practice Test Level 8 - Instructions** Bright Kids NYC Inc ©

# Answer Key

|  | PA | SC | PC | NA | NP | NS | FM | PF | FC |
|---|---|---|---|---|---|---|---|---|---|
| 1. | 1 | 4 | 2 | 3 | 3 | 3 | 1 | 3 | 2 |
| 2. | 3 | 1 | 1 | 1 | 2 | 1 | 2 | 1 | 2 |
| 3. | 2 | 2 | 1 | 1 | 4 | 3 | 3 | 1 | 2 |
| 4. | 3 | 3 | 4 | 1 | 4 | 1 | 3 | 1 | 4 |
| 5. | 1 | 2 | 2 | 2 | 1 | 1 | 2 | 3 | 1 |
| 6. | 3 | 4 | 1 | 3 | 3 | 1 | 2 | 2 | 3 |
| 7. | 1 | 3 | 4 | 1 | 3 | 3 | 2 | 1 | 2 |
| 8. | 1 | 1 | 1 | 2 | 1 | 1 | 1 | 4 | 3 |
| 9. | 3 | 1 | 2 | 3 | 4 | 1 | 1 | 3 | 1 |
| 10. | 1 | 4 | 1 | 1 | 3 | 1 | 2 | 4 | 4 |
| 11. | 1 | 4 | 1 | 2 | 1 | 3 | 1 | 3 | 3 |
| 12. | 1 | 4 | 2 | 1 | 3 | 1 | 2 | 4 | 1 |
| 13. | 3 | 1 | 2 | 3 | 3 | 1 | 1 | 1 | 3 |
| 14. | 2 | 1 | 3 | 1 | 2 | 1 | 3 | 4 | 4 |
| 15. | 1 | 1 | 2 | 1 |  | 1 | 2 | 1 | 1 |
| 16. | 2 | 4 | 3 | 3 |  | 1 | 3 | 1 | 3 |
| 17. | 2 | 2 | 4 | 1 |  | 1 | 2 |  | 2 |
| 18. | 1 | 1 | 4 | 3 |  | 1 | 3 |  | 3 |

**CogAT® Practice Test Level 8 - Instructions**     Bright Kids NYC Inc ©